ALONG THE TRAIL

A Story Of
"One Little Indian"

by Elmer M. Savilla

A. *Steamboats docked at Yuma bringing supplies from Baja California. Circa 1898*

B. *The city of Yuma, flooded in the Spring of 1908.*

C. *Quechan men. Circa 1870*

D. *Quechan leaders display their allegiance by posing with American flag. 1893*

C

D

3

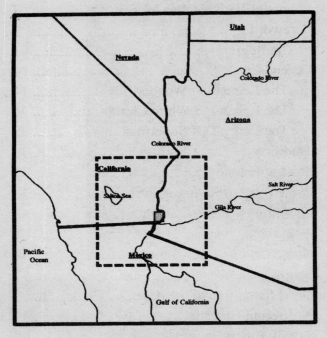

Utah

Nevada

Colorado River

Arizona

Colorado River

California

Salton Sea

Salt River

Gila River

Pacific
Ocean

Mexico

Gulf of California

— — — — Former Quechan homelands

▨ Present day Quechan reservation boundary

 4

CONTENTS

The Quechan Indian Tribe

The Quechan people are one of several Native American tribes known as Yuman. The geographical environment of the area along the lower Colorado River Valley was harsh enough to more or less isolate them socially from the groups of tribes to the west and to the east, although excursions to these areas for trade and warfare purposes did frequently take place.

The exact time of their "emergence" is unknown, however modern scientists agree that there is evidence that for at least the past 10,000 years human activity existed here. Apart from the once densely forested river valley, the geography shows clear evidence of high volcanic activity. The valley is rimmed on both sides by hot desert sands and barren rock hills and mountains for hundreds of miles in all directions except to the south where the Colorado River emptied into the Gulf of California.

It is easy then to imagine why the Colorado River and its green valley well-stocked with fish and game was the center of the Quechan's world.

Phonetics For Quechan Words Used In This Book.

There have been several attempts by interested persons to put the Quechan language into writing, but there is no general agreement as to the precise sounds of vowels, or the pronunciation and spelling of Quechan words. For the purpose of this book we suggest the simple version developed by a Quechan tribal elder, now deceased.

a   sounds like the English obscure a, as in *ability*.

c   sounds like the English sh, as in *shot*.

tc resembles the sound of the English ch, as in *charge*.

x   resembles the sound of the German ch.

n   resembles the English ng, as in *sing*.

e   as in *met*.

i   as in *din*.

o   as in *dot*.

u   as in *hoot*.

'   indicates vowel emphasis.

FOREWORD

This booklet tells of what it was like in the early part of the 1900's for a young Quechan Indian boy to grow up on a Native American Indian reservation. The story is about his early years and his experiences with life as he and his family went through the social transition brought about by first the European and then the American colonization of their Quechan tribe's historic homelands.

It tells a little bit about his tribe's history, their customs and traditions which had been handed down from one generation to the next. This is his point of view from two points in time, before and after the coming of Europeans to this continent, as the boy grew up into manhood in a world his ancestors had never even dreamed of. The importance of this boy's story is that his was the last generation of Quechans to know how things used to be, before 1941 and the beginning of the Nuclear Age.

Indian reservations are still a mystery to most of modern America. In fact Indians themselves are a part of that mystery which has been created because of a mixture of indifference, ignorance and an unwillingness to learn, on the part of non-Indians. Many non-Indians prefer to know only the fictional romanticized view of Indian life imparted from the writings of early western writers and partly from smarmy and not so smarmy films and documentaries. (Dances With Wolves, Broken Arrow, Cheyenne Autumn, et al)

Depending on one's own view gained from history books or early writings, Native Americans were either stoic, heroic, wise, capable of delivering extemporaneous profound speeches, and at one with Nature, or, on the other hand he was a fierce Godless savage, warlike, a killer of white men and kidnapper of blonde, blue-eyed white women. Neither view is correct, of course. Above all, they were human, with the same attributes and frailties seen in other races. No more, no less. This book tries to describe in an understandable way, the real truth about "Indians:" How the people of this one tribe lived and what they believed in the days before the European invasion and what happened afterwards to change their lifestyle forever.

The time described by the writer begins in the years just after the arrival of the Europeans, leading into the acrimonious relationship between the Quechan and the newcomers, then the troublesome times of the late 1890s and the early 1900s when the alien United States Government began to seriously impose its laws and culture on the Quechan Nation, some 30 years after the subjugation of Indian Tribes of the mid-West. We hope it will enlighten the reader and create an understanding of present-day social and political problems which continue to hamper the improvement of community life and the standard of living on many Native American reservations.

The purpose of this book is neither to condemn nor to glorify the actions of any race or persons, but instead it is to impart to the reader a reliable sense of early life on the Quechan reservation

 10

CHAPTER 1

IN THE BEGINNING.

Since time immemorial, the various bands of this continent's native race now known as Native Americans, American Indians or Indian Tribes, knew this land called America as a living thing. It was Mother Earth, *In-ti'-yah*, in the language of the Quechan people, from whose belly they had emerged into the bright light given off by *Anya'*, the Sun. It was *In-ti'-yah* who provided all things needed to sustain life, the air, the soil, the sweet-tasting life-blood water, and all the plants and animals. Each played a part in the others daily life and each had a responsibility for the other. That was the message given to the *Pipah'*, the people, in their ancient stories of Creation which was handed down, generation to generation, in stories in word and in song.

In the Quechan story-songs of the Creation and everyday life, animals and Nature played leading roles in the explanation of how things are and why. The stories were sung by the *scava'rrhuhai* (singer) in a series of songs which told the legend and sung in an "old" language which was not understood by most people, but the stories were told in the language of the time.

Some of these story-songs took at least nine hours to complete and some were even longer. The subjects of those songs include:

Coyote in legend and story-song is a cunning and sly being who specialized in living off the efforts of others.

Quail, the beautiful desert bird, lived clustered in flocks in the thick brush for protection and coming out to search for food in the early morning hours and the time just before sunset. It was not unusual to see 100 or more birds feeding while three or more male birds stood guard high in the trees, sounding the alarm when danger approached.

Roadrunner was a curious and elusive scavenger who would follow the traveler long distances for no apparent reason, then holler in a staccato chatter of disgust when the traveler discarded nothing edible.

Rattlesnake appeared only at night to hunt for rodents. He served the Quechan as a messenger to the lower world by descending each winter through tunnels dug for him by other small animals.

And there was the prankster, Lightning Boy, who on summer nights could be seen running through the clouds, and jumping from hill to faraway hill like an impatient young boy unable to sit still in front of an audience, always showing off. He was the world's first hyperactive child, shouting "Look at me, see what I can do," as he jumped here, now there.

Some legends were about birds, the coyote, the deer, a frog, and lightning. Other songs which were sung for social dancing and remembrance ceremonies were about corn and the people.

The legend about their creation tells of how *Kukumat* created them along with the Cocopah, Kamias, Maricopa and Mojave people. Their place of emergence from the lower world was the huge and towering mountain of stone now known as Newberry Mountain, north of Needles, California. The Quechan call it *Avikwame'*. All resided in the lush valley created over the millennia by the mighty river which would someday be known as the Colorado. Thereafter there appeared supernatural beings in human and animal form who taught them the natural rules by which they must live.

These legends in story-song form were committed to memory by certain singers, then told and retold down through the generations. For a short period of time beginning in about 1945 and through 1985, the stories and songs almost faded from memory, but as of this writing in 1996 they are beginning to come back. In the next chapter, three of those Quechan legends are described.

CHAPTER 2

LEGENDS

The Legend Of Wonder Boy

There once was two boys who were children of a bird called *wi'tsawits*. It is a common bird with a yellow breast that comes round in the spring. The boys were named *A'xtakwa'some* and *Pu'kuhan*.

They went to find material to make a flute. One boy said to the other "when I play this flute the girls will love me." When the flute was finished he played a song to celebrate. The words of the song were "I have the flute in my mouth. Anyone living far away will hear and come to listen to me."

Their boyhood was spent in learning many things. When they grew into manhood they each took two wives. The younger man soon died and the family journeyed to the east. During the journey one of the older man's wives gave birth to a child.

An old blind man who was the father of the dead man's wives disliked the older man who was the flute player. The blind man said that if the child was a boy, he would kill him, but if it were a girl he would keep her because she could cook and bring him water. A baby boy was born. This was Wonder Boy because it was known that he would have special powers. Among the Quechan it was not unusual for a man to change names several times.

The mother of the child had great medicine power so she caused the child's crying to sound like that of a girl baby. This saved the boy's life. Later, the boy was given the name *"Mitpa'khumi"* by Coyote, who was his paternal uncle. He was not satisfied with this name so he decided to find a name that he liked. So he began to travel in order to find the new name.

As he traveled, the name came to him and he announced in a song that "This day I will be called throughout the world *"Po'kohan."*

Later in his travels, he returned to the place where he was born. The willow and arrow weed hut was deserted and there was only bird and snake tracks around it. He put his hands over his closed eyes and stood there for a long time. When he opened his eyes he saw the ceremonial garments of his ancestors hanging on the walls. He saw a war bonnet decorated with feathers, he put it on and went outdoors to admire it. He then took it off and put it back on the wall.

He kept one small piece of bamboo called *"axta'kasa."* He said, "this was used by my ancestors and let them go a long time without drinking water. I will take it and use it in my travels." He took another thing called *"ha'punor"*, a belt, and said "This will help me to go without food." He took a war bonnet saying "This will keep the sun off my head." He also took a bag which he carried over his shoulder. He then continued his travel.

He now had a desire to see his ancestors. He stopped, made a fire, then poured water on it. He piled the hot, wet ashes into a small mound and ran his hand through it and brought out his father who had died before his birth. His father did not look human, but Wonder Boy recognized him. His father spoke to him, "I am glad to see you, my son, but remember that my shin bones are being used as shinny sticks by others (shinny is a stick-ball game similar to hockey). The man who killed me caused me to inhale much dust so I would become dry and unable to come to life again." Wonder Boy told him, "It's all right, father, I have the power to bring you back to life but I will not do it. This shall be an example to others for all future years." (If Wonder Boy had restored his father to life it would have been possible for every human to be restored to life by medicine power)

Then the boy put his father back into the ashes.

Wonder Boy traveled on, but he was still not satisfied. He thought that if he brought his father back one more time and talked to him, he would

 16

be satisfied. He brought his father back and they wept in each others arms. After that, he felt satisfied. Then his father told him, "In my life, I stored a lot of dried deer meat and other food at a certain mountain. Go there and take everything I stored and use it on your travel."

Wonder Boy replied, "No. What you did, what you wore, and what you stored I do not want to take. I have my own power to provide for myself." So when his father was put back into the ashes the wind blew dust and clouds, and thunder roared as he went into the earth forever.

Wonder Boy traveled on and soon arrived at the (Colorado) river. He traveled south to see if he could find a narrow place where he could cross the river. Finding none, he turned toward the north.

He saw a piece of petrified wood. He wrapped his belongings and tried to cross the river on the wood. He had not known that petrified wood was too heavy to float. He was sinking as he tried to hold up the wood and his belongings. Just as he was about to drown he was caught in a whirlpool and carried to the other side of the river. He put his clothes back on and took one step and found himself on top of *"Avik'wame."*

While standing on top of the mountain he remembered what his uncle Coyote had told him. "In your travels through deserts and unknown lands if you happen to swallow your saliva you will become lost in your wanderings." This saying kept coming into his mind, but he knew where he was and knew the name of the mountain, so how could he be lost? He announced that "this is my country and this mountain belongs to me."

He then decided to travel west and started to run down the mountain and immediately found that he was already at another mountain called *"Celai't."* As he stood there in thought, he decided then to go toward the place called *"Pika'tco"* (present day Picacho Peak) for this would be a shortcut for him to the site on the east side of the river (near the present City of Yuma). He came to a place which he named *"Avi'apsin."*

Wonder Boy was still not satisfied so he wandered on until he reached a place called *"A'matiya,"* which meant Earth Mouth. He stood there awhile, then saw something moving through the water to the other bank. It was dressed in bamboo and had rings on its fingers which were made of bamboo and it wore bamboo sandals. A piece of bamboo stuck up from its hair like a feather.

He thought, "I will hide and then catch it. If it is an animal I will keep it for a pet, and if it is a human I will consider him as a friend." While he was hiding, the thing moved closer to him. He saw then that it was exactly like Wonder Boy, only it was dressed differently. He then saw it was his half-brother *A'xtakwa'some,* who had as much power as he had although he didn't know this.

When he came closer he tried to grab him. The stranger suddenly disappeared and then reappeared on a sandbar on the other side. Wonder Boy then recognized him and said, "I am your half-brother, and the person who has told me this is my uncle *"Hatpaakwas."* (Coyote)

The stranger said nothing, not convinced, and stood there with tears in his eyes. They talked of bringing his uncle to prove their relationship. After awhile, the stranger was convinced. Wonder Boy took off his garment and wrapped it in a stone and threw it to the stranger on the other side. The stranger said, "I understand now how it is, and you show me much respect, but I have nothing to give you in return, nothing but this bamboo."

They then parted, the stranger going to the west and Wonder Boy went to the south. After a distance, Wonder Boy stopped and said, "I will sing for him for the last time." He sang of his half-brother by his name, *"Ahtakwasome."*

He then continued on until he saw a jack rabbit sleeping in the path. He almost stepped on it and it started to run toward the mesa. It then stopped, stood on its hind legs, and looked at Wonder Boy. Wonder Boy was still a small boy and he was frightened by the rabbit. So he said, "I will destroy this grass that you feed on so that you can never come here again to feed," yet the boy knew it would grow back even if he did destroy it.

The boy lit fire to the grass and it began to burn. He thought then "If I could only get rid of my hair it would not be so heavy." So he put his head into the fire and burned off his hair. He took the small piece of bamboo (to prevent thirst) and put in his mouth, and put the belt (to prevent hunger) around his waist. He put the war bonnet on his head, but it would not stay on because he had no hair. He thought, "Why didn't I think of that before? Now I have no use for this war bonnet." But on a second thought he spit on the palm of his right hand then put the bonnet on his right hand and then on his head. It stayed on.

He traveled some more and came to a big gully. He heard a loud, yet low, sound. He lay on the ground and watched until the sound came to him and he saw that it was a wildcat. He called the wildcat *"Naxme."* Its body was striped and its eyes shone bright. This was the first naming of this animal.

Farther on he met a humming bird. It made a sound like there was more than one bird. He named this bird *"Nakui'x."*

He traveled farther on and heard another strange sound. It came from an insect, (what we call a horsefly today), which he named *"Huau'.*

As can be seen, this particular legend of Wonder Boy and his adventures and the naming of the birds and animals, could go on for some time, and it does. Each part of the story has a song that describes the story and the song can be repeated several times according to the whim of the story teller. The full Wonder Boy series takes about nine hours to complete.

The Legend of White Cloud.

Akwe'kwaxma'l, White Cloud, controls the lightning, thunder and storms. White Cloud would appear to certain medicine men in a dream and would give them power to bring rain or to cause a sand storm. If a man with these powers were with a war party he could summon a sand storm to conceal the warriors.

In the Quechan and nearby Cocopah legends there are several stories about where storms and lightning come from. One such story, complete with a series of accompanying songs, tells about a certain bug which also has power over a storm. This bug may also appear in a man's dream and teach him songs. In the dream the bug drags his tail on the ground, wiggles it vigorously and causes the dust to rise. As he speaks and gives commands, the dust will increase until it covers the earth.

Another story tells of a boy named *Kwayawhumar* who lived up in the sky where it is all frozen snow. In the spring, he would go hunting and whenever he would draw his bow it caused lightning and when the arrow hit its mark it caused thunder.

Here we tell you about the better known legend of White Cloud.

White Cloud has only one bow and one arrow. He holds it up and wherever he swings the bow, in any direction, it causes lightning and when he moves his body it causes thunder.

When a human medicine man who has the power given to him by White Cloud in a dream wishes to bring on a sand storm, he would make a speech known only to himself and then he would sing a song. Immediately the storm would come. This story and songs about lightning is said to be dangerous for others to hear.

In one of the more popular story-songs about lightning, it tells of how White Cloud saw a distant mountain (near the present site of Indio, California) and he traveled toward it. He named the mountain *Avi'tinya'm,* which means Dark Mountain.

After a while, White Cloud left Dark Mountain and went up into the air, making a path in the sky. At last he found a place in the sky which pleased him so well that he called it his home. But he wondered aloud of how he could make a living there, but this was only a pretense because he already knew what he would do.

He noticed that every time he sang his song in the early hours of night, bats would come out and dance as he sang. As he sang he noticed clouds circling above him and he thought it was smoke. While standing there he saw a bird called *Meru'si* and asked the bird where he had been. The bird told him he had just come from the east. In honor of the bird, White Cloud sang throughout the night. The next morning White Cloud said he was happy and satisfied with all he had seen, and now he would demonstrate his own magic power which would be seen in the sky by others.

White Cloud said he would now be known by the lightning, thunder, and rain in the sky, and they would continue although he himself might go away. He called to the clouds, the lightning, and the high winds. They came at his command and filled the sky. Still satisfied, White Cloud returned to his new home and sang his new songs.

A time passed and White Cloud decided to travel again. Before leaving, he sang of his proposed travel to the south. When he began to travel, at a certain place in the sky he saw a woodpecker and said to it, "Now I know that creatures such as you live and roam on the earth," and he sang a song to the woodpecker.

He traveled farther and found himself over the ocean where he saw great waves throwing mist into the sky and he created a song to remember this sight. He declared, "This place is the beginning of the clouds, the high winds, and the thunder. I alone can command them to appear." He sang of his power in the skies.

He still lives there, and although he is never seen, the things which he calls up, clouds, winds, and thunder, lets one know he is still powerful.

In the telling of this story, there are a group of songs which help to tell the story to listeners. Only certain men know these songs and are usually reluctant to sing them to outsiders. One such man is known to have allowed an outsider to record two songs. This caused him so much worry that he could not rest or sleep for awhile. Although the story is a simple one, one of the reasons why the story telling takes more than just a few hours is that almost every new action on the part of the subject, or his meeting with other people or animals, has a song that must be sung.

Examples of some songs from this lightning story include: "I have arrived in the sky;" "The sky is in darkness;" "On top of his own mountain;" and "At the end of the path in the sky." There are many more songs in this series without which the story would lose much of its mysticism for listeners.

The Legend Of Superman

It was said that in the beginning there were two beings who rose from the bottom of the earth. Once caused light and created human beings, and the other was destructive and was therefore called "Superman," or in Quechan his name was *Koma'stamho*. This particular story is about the death of Superman and his cremation. It is said that after his death, some of the people changed into birds and animals, but the next generation were entirely human beings.

After a long and hard life, Superman was in a serious condition, but he would not admit to anyone that he was sick. His children surrounded him and sat at his side and asked him to tell them about his illness.

Superman would not talk of illness and said that he was not sick. In doing so he set an example for future wise men to follow, and to this day such men will never admit that they are sick, even though they may be near death. But his children continued to insist that he was very sick.

It was soon evident that Superman was rapidly growing worse, so his children said to him, "You are passing away. Your eyes show that you are growing weaker and yet you do not seem to hear what we are saying. We still ask and beg you to speak to us for the last time."

The children beseeched him, saying that he seemed to like the ground on which he lay since he had no inclination to rise from the ground, and this was a sign that the person would soon pass away. A bug tried to ease his suffering by digging into the ground and bringing up cool sand which it placed on his chest, but this had no effect.

Finally Superman spoke and said, "I love you, my children, so much that I do not wish to speak, and at the same time I feel as though I were sleepy and could never have any life in me again." He continued, "As I have said before, and in addition to what I have already said, I have in my mind the four corners of the earth. Among these I may choose the place to which my spirit will go, but I have not yet chosen."

Then the children took hold of his legs and laid him with his feet toward the east. He lay in that position but was not satisfied, so they turned him with his feet toward the north. He said, "No, I do not choose this position." So they turned him toward the west and after lying there he refused to stay in that direction. They then laid him with his feet toward the south, and in that position he held himself until he passed away in a few moments. In taking this position he had set an example to coming generations, showing that when they die their spirits will go towards the south. The children then prepared for his cremation.

While the cremation fire burned brightly, Coyote traveled toward the place. It is said that this coyote was one of the very worst and wild sort that anyone will ever see. The animals were standing in a circle around the fire and the buzzard asked them all to stand firmly and keep as close together as possible, but there was some animals that were very short. Coyote knew this and he planned to break through the circle at this point.

After Coyote arrived he requested the animals in the circle to kindly spread out so that he would have room to get inside and to circle four times around the fire, after which he would find a place where he could stand and cry, as everyone did at these cremation ceremonies. But it was whispered from one animal to another to keep their own positions and not move to let Coyote in.

Coyote had planned to seize the heart of Superman and he thought it would not burn him. The female buzzard warned the animals, "Coyote is somewhere near, though we cannot see him. We must prevent whatever he tries to do."

The animals kept as close together as possible, but Coyote jumped over the line and seized the heart of Superman, which had not yet burned. He jumped out of the circle at the same place where he had entered and ran as fast as he could toward the east. The buzzard said, "I knew something of this sort would happen. Now that Coyote has taken Superman's heart I don't know what to do."

When Coyote had traveled a long distance he stopped on a mountain. He ate the heart and became unconscious with a powerful spell cast over him. He died immediately.

Another version of the death of Superman is sometimes told: When Superman died, the people surrounded him because they had never seen anything like this before. This was the first time they had seen death. They stood and looked at him. Then came a large worm who said, "I will make a light." He took some willow bark and an arrow-weed stalk which he twisted. He made a spark and the willow bark burned and everyone could see. The bright light was reflected in the eastern sky and looked like a star.

Before Superman had died he had made a wish. "I wish that Coyote would take after my heart and do what is right." Coyote misunderstood the wish and thought he was to actually take his heart. The people knew Coyote had the wrong idea and the medicine woman tried to trick him. When the worm's bright light was seen in the east, she said to Coyote, "Go, flash your tail in this light and get some fire for the cremation." Coyote went away. While he was gone the people piled up the cremation logs, put Superman's body on it and lit the fire with the worm's light. Thus the cremation was started while Coyote was gone. When he returned the fire was blazing and the four tribes were there to sympathize with the friends of the dead.

The friends stood so close together around the fire that Coyote could not get in. He walked round and round the crowd and as he walked he came to the place where Skunk, Coon, Badger, and Gopher stood. They were so short that he leaped over them. The cremation was only about half finished. He snatched the heart out of the body and ran away with it to the top of another peak (west of the present site of Tempe, Arizona).

He rested there and laid down the heart and it stained the peak with his blood, so it is known to this day as *Vi'ikwahas,* which means "stained peak," or "greasy peak." From there he ran to another peak which was on the shore of the ocean. Then he went to an island in the ocean which had a peak and there he ate the heart of Superman, and there he died. That island is still called *Vi'niwa,* from *wa* meaning heart, and *vi* meaning peak.

CHAPTER 3

TRADITIONS

The Quechan people had a profound respect for all things belonging to *In-ti'-yah,* Mother Earth. They understood that *Pipah',* the people, could really own none of those things which were Hers. The water which gave them fish and quenched their thirst was Her blood; the pure desert air which was necessary for life was Her breath, and the soil which grew the delicious watermelons, maize, squash, and white beans was Her body. They owed their very life to Her and they knew that one day they would have to give it back. The sun which warmed the earth and all its plants, birds, and animals, was called *Anya'.*

Giving thanks to *In-ti'-yah* each day for these things was their form of religion, this was their way of life. Mother Earth and Father Sun, *Anya'* had been their creators and after their "emergence" from *Avikwame',* the Sacred Place, they were told to live according to certain rules set down by Nature, their Uncle. Nature was the overseer and regulator of natural law. Their reason for living was not of their own making. They had to each find their own path and purpose in life and each found their individual role in the overall plan of life through spiritual contact with the Creators. Through ceremonies and prayers taught them they would ask for guidance and when the individual was ready and able to receive, they would be given a sign which only they could recognize.

Every creature and every person knew that at some point in time they might be required to give up their own life for the benefit of some other creature or person so that the other might live. This was the wish of *In-ti'-yah'*.

For centuries, the Quechan had lived happily, with no one person laying down rules for living. The Quechan were indeed "free spirits." *In-ti'-yah* had made the rules and if there was a prolonged violation of her rules Nature would exact a high price on the individual. There were no lawyers, judges, or courts of law where bargains could be struck. There were only the infallible rules set down by *In-ti'-yah,* and there was always just one punishment. Coyote, Rattlesnake, or even Lightning Boy would see to that. But all one had to do to enjoy a bountiful life was to follow the simple rules laid down and enforced by Nature and one could expect, after certain lessons were learned, to join their ancestors in that place known to non-Indians as "Heaven." They could expect that upon their death, they would be transported to the other place by the smoke from their own cremation fire.

It is interesting and fondly remembered that the young boy whose story begins in Chapter 7 once asked his father what happened when a person died. He said in a matter of fact way that "The relatives already know he is on his way to see them. They wait there with a feast of the best watermelons and sweet corn. After a long visit everyone goes about their usual business, but there is a lot of dancing that goes on and everyone has a good time every day." After that, at each cremation the boy witnessed, he could visualize the relatives standing (on what?) waiting for the person to come through a hole in the clouds.

CHAPTER 4

STRANGE PEOPLE

And so it was, until one day at a certain place and time, a strange looking huge canoe with huge wind-catchers attached arrived at a far away eastern shore of the land. The Quechan knew nothing of this landing but the effect reached them when in a few years they witnessed the arrival of strange looking men with pale skins and hair on their faces, wearing shiny metal coats and riding animals which they called *"caballo,"* a horse. Later, hordes of other pale people came to the land of the Quechan on horseback, by horse-drawn wagon, then by river boats which had clouds of smoke pouring out of them. Still they were not alarmed. Some of the new arrivals wore heavy robes which must have been very hot in the desert air. They told the Quechan that they came from someone they called God and said they were here to save something called their "soul." All of these things were taken in stride by the Quechan and they quickly learned to adapt to their new neighbors.

There were no Quechan words for, or understanding of, "invasion," and so the strange-looking people were welcomed and treated like relatives.

In *In-ti'-yah's* teachings, all men and women were "family," and these newcomers were just the funny looking ones with strange ways. Every family knows that kind.

These newcomers tried to explain to the natives, who were now called "Indians" because of the mistaken belief of the captain of that first sailing ship that he had reached a place called India, that they, the pale-looking ones with hairy faces, had "discovered" the Quechan and their ancestral lands, and that they were now the owners of this new and beautiful land and that they now made the laws by which the Quechan must live.

Some would call this desert land harsh, but the Quechan had adapted to the hot sunlight and dry desert air and lived comfortably in the forests of willow, cottonwood, mesquite, and bamboo which grew on both sides of the river in a valley made rich and fertile by annual spring floods which left deposits of silt from upstream. Here they planted their crops of maize, melons, squash, and tepary beans. The thorny mesquite trees gave them pods of sweet tasting beans and a sticky sap of many uses. The willow bark furnished a strong and flavorful tea which worked to keep one healthy, and the desert sage gave them medicine for all kinds of ailments. With bows of willow and arrows made from the straight and slender arrow-weed, they hunted the many forms of game which *In-ti'-yah* had placed here. And of course, like all humans, they frequently argued and fought with their neighbors.

The Quechan did not understand the concept of owning the earth or things of the earth and so did not, at first, argue against the claim of discovery and subsequent ownership. The Indians had been willing to share the land and its blessings. There was enough of everything to go around and they had no ill-will towards these strangers. Weren't all men brothers and didn't they know of Mother Earth, Father Sun and Nature's laws?

Accordingly, the strangers were made welcome. The land and its resources were shared with them, and not until it was too late did they become aware that a gradual and unnoticed encroachment had taken place and that the laws of *In-ti'-yah* had been replaced by laws made by the newcomers. Worse, the Indians were expected to comply, part and parcel with these new laws and without question. A new chapter in the long history of Man had arrived in the land of the Quechan. The Quechan chose to cooperate with the new arrivals, believing that *In-ti'-yah* would not have allowed this to happen if it were not Her will and for the better.

Mercifully, the Quechan knew nothing of the white man's violent and bloody history in their own homelands and so did not forcefully resist. If *In-ti'-yah* had willed it, or even had allowed them to fight the invaders, it is certain that against the new and terrible weapons which they called "guns, bullets and cannon" that their primitive hunting weapons of willow bows, reed arrows, spears and stone slings would have been useless, as would be proven later in time, and they would not have survived to this day.

With new lessons to learn and with a growing understanding of what they were now up against from those calling themselves Spaniards, and then the Americans, the Quechan cooperated and sometimes used the white man's own laws against them. They had found that some of the whites, the ones who wore the hot robes and spoke of God, had a knowledge and a practice of the Creators moral laws and did attempt to live by them. They would use those laws and these people to protect as much of their homelands as they could to perpetuate the Quechan. It was the will of *In-ti'-yah* that they do this, it was said, because in Her wisdom She knew that at some future time, the laws of Nature would again prevail and Her native people would be needed to teach the laws to those who chose to honor Her, and to rebuild what had been lost.

CHAPTER 5

FINAL YEARS OF ROAMING FREE

In 1540, the Spaniard Alarcon was the first European to pass their way. In the early 1770's the Spaniards chose this section of the Colorado River near the Quechan lands, at what is now Yuma, Arizona, to use as a river crossing for settlers and supplies on their way to California. At this point, the river is channeled into a convergence only about 300 yards wide. As the river rushed down from the northern mountains and high plateaus it gathered up small rocks, pebbles and sand which scoured the river bed even wider and deeper. When it reached the softer desert sand near Needles, California, the river widened so that in flood times it was sometimes a mile wide or more in some stretches above and below Fort Yuma.

At this spot, huge rock formations on both sides of the river resisted the river and acting as a dam, forced it into a narrow stream, creating a wide stretch of water upstream which varied in width depending on the amount of winter rain and snow which had fallen in the northern mountains. It was the only place for hundreds of miles upstream from the Gulf of California where the river

37

was narrow enough to be safely crossed on rafts in times when it was not in flood stage. The Spaniards soon recognized the value of this spot as had the Quechan before them. It became a hub for travelers between Mexico, New Mexico Territory and California.

Early European relations with American Indian Tribes was governed by the laws of nations, international law. The Spanish, French, Dutch, and English had agreed that American Indians "were people able to reason and capable of conversion to Christianity" and that their rights to the land they occupied would be given due consideration. The Quechan knew nothing of that agreement and took no pains to mark off any boundaries of land which they owned, and they knew nothing of the struggle between the European nations for control and ownership of "the new world." It may be helpful to the reader, then, to briefly explain the early relationship between the Indian Tribes and the newcomers.

Historian S. Lyman Tyler tells us that although the French, Dutch, English, and American governments did make some attempt to recognize and protect Indian lands from settlers, it was the Spanish who made the most vigorous attempts to protect them. Another historian, Frederick Hall, said in that regard that "The broad field of Spanish jurisprudence bristled with fortifications for the protection of Indians." However, it must be noted that the Spanish conquistador and the Spanish missionary often were in conflict with each other. One wanted to use them for a source of labor, and the other wanted to convert them. Although they were placed in a "wardship" status the Spanish Crown ordered that Indians be recognized as fellow subjects and as "free persons" with legal rights. In fact, the Crown made the enslavement of Indians illegal as was their use for personal services.

It was inevitable that as more settlers would arrive, colonial expansion would occur and nations would quarrel over land ownership. Indians being the weaker, the European nation would extend their "protection" for the Indians and establish jurisdiction over the Indian lands. It is notable that the United States, more than any other nation, continually increased its jurisdiction over Indian lands in spite of having recognized their sovereignty by negotiating and then signing treaties with them. Until at least 1849 the Quechan were able to live as they had for centuries, mainly undisturbed by the outside world which would soon descend upon them.

Before 1821, the entire southwest region, including what is now California (from San Francisco southward), Arizona, New Mexico, and Texas, was Spanish territory and in general the relationship between the Quechan and the Spanish was not confrontational but there were notable exceptions. One of the exceptions occurred in July of 1781. The Spaniards had begun two small settlements, called "pueblo's," near the river. As the Spanish population grew, they began to abuse Quechan hospitality and on July 18 the Indians attacked and destroyed both pueblo's and a Catholic mission which had been proselytizing natives. After this, the Spanish avoided antagonizing the Quechan further because of logistic and reinforcement difficulties and things remained peaceful.

In 1821, Mexico won its independence from Spain and assumed control of the formerly Spanish territories. Mexico made everyone, including the Indians, citizens of Mexico whether they wanted this or not. In fact, it is doubtful that any Indians realized that they were Mexican citizens and what it meant. Later when California, Arizona and New Mexico became part of the United States, the Mexican citizenship of the Indians became a recognition problem for many of the tribes. It wasn't until 1893 that the United States signed an Agreement with the Quechan which recognized their jurisdiction and land ownership. On June 2, 1924, the Quechan were made citizens of the U.S.

In the meantime the American westward expansion was underway. In 1848 the war between the United States and Mexico ended when The Treaty of Guadalupe Hidalgo was signed. A southern border of the U.S. was formed and all

Mexican lands north of that border became American territory. In that treaty, the U.S. agreed to recognize the sovereignty of Indian Tribes within their new lands. With the signing of that treaty, and later, in spite of it, the door was opened to the settlement and development of the region and the lifestyle of the Quechan people slowly began to change.

Where before Spain and Mexico had made sincere efforts to maintain a peaceful relationship with the Quechan, with the coming of gold-seekers and settlers seeking land, the Quechan's freedom to roam throughout the region and to maintain their easy going lifestyle was destined to end.

CHAPTER 6

LEARNING HOW TO LIVE ON A RESERVATION

In the years prior to 1927 the river channel just north of what is now Yuma, Arizona changed its course almost yearly according to the whim of flood waters as it slowly scoured out a new bed. During this period of time in the mid-1800s, the river came out of the north and swung eastward, then an abrupt right turn to the west as it skirted the hills of Yuma. It then rushed through the narrow rock channel between Yuma, Arizona and Fort Yuma, California.

On the west side of the Colorado River at this point, was a hill which had withstood the river's force. It stood about 100 feet above the flat flood plain. After gold was discovered in California in 1849, the U.S. Army chose to establish a military fort on top of this hill as a means to provide safety for gold miners, settlers and traders traveling through to the California gold fields. This was the first U.S. encroachment on Quechan land without their permission. Three companies of the 2nd Infantry set up their camp atop what is known as "Indian Hill" overlooking the Quechan lands. Thus Fort Yuma came into being.

The Quechan took a dim view of this fort and created some problems for the army by harassing supply trains. Food and supplies were hard to get, so in 1851 the U.S. Army was forced to withdraw. In 1852 the army returned with reinforcements and new supplies were assured because of the beginning of river steamboats coming upstream from the rivers mouth in lower California. By this time the Quechan were described as "warlike" by Brevet Major S. P. Heintzelman. This was the first military outpost which the Quechan had ever seen and life for them and the soldiers was made more difficult because of a mutual dislike. But over a short period of time the Quechan adjusted to both the presence of the soldiers and to a new town being built across the river.

On the southern side of the river, a town sprang up which provided a resting place for travelers and merchants who brought in building supplies and food. The town was first called Colorado City and had only a blacksmith, a supply store, and a saloon. In 1858 a Butterfield stage coach route stopped here on its way to California. But the town was short lived. In 1862, the river flooded and washed everything down stream into Mexico. The town was rebuilt and named Arizona City. It survived.

By 1873 there were five river steamboats carrying supplies and passengers to Arizona City and further upstream to Needles, California. From this new development traffic the town's population rose to a booming 1300. Arizona City became a virtual seaport, a major point for passengers and freight to and from San Francisco, by way of the Gulf of California. In 1875 the town's name was again changed, this time to Yuma. Arizona was not yet a state, so the region was called Arizona Territory. The railroad had also come to Yuma in 1870 and its future was assured as an important station on the cross-country railroad.

More and more, the lifestyle of the Quechan was forced to change. Even their choice of food was now limited. They were introduced to sugar, flour, and other fatty foods, and of course, liquor. At the same time their access to traditional native foods was being restricted.

At first, during the time up to 1890, there was some internal tribal turmoil because of outside influence on who should speak for the Quechan. The military had selected an Indian person who served their purpose to speak for the tribe. Later when the fort was transferred to the Catholic Church a nun by the name of Mary O'Neil was named as the federal governments Superintendent of the Indian School. She then selected whom she would recognize as the Quechan leader. In some respects this is a practice which has perpetuated itself. Today all duly elected tribal leaders have to be approved and recognized by the local agency of the Bureau of Indian Affairs and the Secretary of

Interior. Clearly an intrusion into local government and a denial of democracy.

By 1883 the majority of the Quechan no longer had the desire to resist the new development and most of them stayed where they were, content in living their daily lives as best they could. In doing so they remained quite primitive, causing outsiders to consider them less than equals. Only those men who wore the Anglo clothing and seemed to cooperate with the new development were tolerated outside of the reservation. Some of the Quechan had accepted the new environment and began to take jobs with the railroad, on the steamboats, or with private businesses in the town of Yuma.

In 1884, the U.S. Army decided it was no longer necessary to maintain Fort Yuma as a military post and the fort was transferred to the Office of Indian Affairs in Washington. Before the fort was closed down, the U.S. set aside land for the Quechan reservation on the east side of the river. (The rivers course at this point had changed from east to west, to north to south)

Most of the Quechan would have had to move their villages if they accepted the new reservation. They refused to move—preferring to be on the west side of the river—so they stayed where they were. The U.S. was eager to settle them permanently so in March of 1884, 45,000 acres was set aside for them, most of which was in California.

None of the acreage was irrigable at the time so life would become harder for them over the next few years. If the river flooded as it usually did, they would have nowhere to go. They would now have to turn from "free spirits" able to wander freely to the north, south, east, or west, for hunting or trading purposes or to visit their distant relatives, to a lifestyle completely foreign to them. There were no assurances that they could now live off the land. But they trusted that *In-ti-yah* knew what was best for them.

The reservation era which had been imposed on eastern and midwestern tribes beginning in 1870, had caught up with the Quechan, children of *Kukumat,* and they like the others, were unprepared for what was to come.

CHAPTER 7

A QUECHAN FAMILY

Dawn was just beginning to announce the coming of *Anya'*, the sun, when a boy who was barely four years old came out of the house and looked to the east. It was a cool spring morning, one made for living. He raised his arms towards the sky and stretched his body skyward. He learned to do this from his father who always did this first thing in the morning. He didn't know why, but he knew one thing, it felt good. In a few years he would learn that it was an acknowledgment that all warmth and life came from the east and *Anya'* made all things grow. It was sort of like a prayer, his father would tell him. Prayers, outside of solemn ceremonies, were not usually spoken but were instead things done privately in recognition of spiritual powers who made life sweet.

The beautiful blue morning glory blooms planted at each corner of the house seemed to join him in welcoming the morning sun as they all seemed to turn in unison towards the warmth and light of *Anya'*.

No sooner had he raised his arms when a dog came to greet him. This was Jerry, "a red-haired mutt," his father had said when he had brought the dog home and told the boy that it was his play-mate. Jerry had immediately become attached to the boy and they became "best friends," wandering and exploring the wonders of their world each day. They would wander so far afield sometimes that only the dog would know how to get back home.

The boy's family was made up of his father, whom everyone called Cy. His mother, whom all the siblings simply called "Momma." Then there was Al, his older brother who was four years older than he. His sister, two years older, was named Eleanor, but everybody called her "Alley." Within the next four years, two younger sisters, Lily and Marie, would join the family.

Cy was a butcher at the local Fort Yuma grocery store. Momma was an aggressive and ambitious Indian woman who spent her time improving their home and raising food for the table. She had managed to buy a sow which would provide them with meat for the table. She bought a Jersey cow which gave pitchers of milk each day. From the two acres on which their neat little house made of willow logs, arrow weed and clay was located, she managed to always have some kind of crop growing. One time it would be wheat, the next corn and beans. Something was always growing.

Cy had raised some objection when Momma received something called a "brooder" from the Sears-Roebuck mail-order company, but he later approved of it wholeheartedly when he saw what it

 48

would be used for. The brooder was a 3-foot-square sheet metal affair which had four stacked sections to it. The sides were made of galvanized screen. Everyone was told that it would be used to first hatch eggs into little chicks, then raise them until they were old enough to be outside and scratch for themselves.

The weather was still cool so she insisted on setting it up indoors. When the several dozen "fertile" eggs hatched, everyone gathered to enjoy their furry cuteness and continuous chirping. They were white leghorn chickens, Momma said, and they would later give the family eggs for break-fast, chicken for Sunday dinners and what they couldn't eat she would sell, she said. Momma always planned way ahead of everyone else. In a few days the chicks were ready to go outside.

But the most popular crop was when she was able to buy enough strawberry plants to cover about an acre of ground. Momma planted the strawberries and later everyone had to help pull weeds so the berries could grow. And grow they did. They were just beginning to turn red when the first "hobo" from the nearby railroad was seen to be picking a few berries. Momma immediately ran out and physically chased him away with Jerry's help. After that it had been necessary to tie Jerry near the patch at night to scare the hobos away. From then on it was part of the boys chores to keep an eye on the berry patch, especially after a freight train had passed through.

CHAPTER 8

HOME ON THE RESERVATION

In these times of the early 1930s, white America was in the grip of a severe economic depression and the freight trains carried hundreds of unemployed men, mostly blacks and whites, traveling cross-country seeking jobs. Some of these itinerants were called *tramps* and others were *hobos*. There was a difference, Momma said. Tramps would come to the door and ask for food in exchange for work, chopping wood, for instance, but hobo's were "white trash" because they were always begging and stealing, not wanting to work.

There was one white tramp who deserves to be remembered. Murphy appeared at their front door one summer day and said he would chop wood for a hot meal. Momma would never turn anyone away who wanted to work. She fed Murphy the best chicken dinner he probably ever had, because he would reappear several times during the year and rest a while from his travels. He would stay for several days doing work around the house and then suddenly he would be gone. He was a vagabond, a true tramp. This continued for several years. You always knew when he was back, he

50

always arrived at night, because Jerry would bark until he recognized him, then he would talk "dog talk" to him. Cy would wake up, listen for a minute, and then announce, "Murphy's back." Then, one year he never came back.

Cy was a full-blooded native Quechan, born on the Quechan Indian reservation in September of 1900. Momma was a native of the Pueblo people in New Mexico. She had been born in a small pueblo village south of Albuquerque, called Isleta. They had met in Los Angeles in the 1920s, where she had been sent to work for a rich family as a housemaid.

Cy was a musician, having been taught to play band instruments by Catholic nuns at the Fort Yuma Indian School. When the U.S. Army had abandoned the fort they arranged for the Catholic Church to take it over and operate it as a military-style school for Quechan children. Here the boys were taught simple skills and to play band instruments. Girls were taught the usual, sewing and home economics. The boys had to wear military uniforms while at the school.

At the start of World War I, several of the Quechan men had enlisted in the U.S. Navy and because they were already musicians, they served as the ship's band on the battleship U.S.S. California. After his discharge from the Navy, Cy went to Los Angeles and played trombone in dance bands until he met Momma and they decided to marry and raise a family on the Quechan reservation. So they left Los Angeles and went to Fort Yuma, where in a few years five children were born to them.

In the 1930s, living conditions on the Quechan reservation were still primitive compared to things in the non-Indian towns nearby the reservation. There were few American-style frame houses, no running water or plumbing for household use and no indoor toilets and definitely no electricity. But no one complained.

The typical Indian house was a square structure with willow poles at the corners and on the overhead ceiling. Open window and door frames were often as not covered with cloth but which allowed free passage of both humans and animals, but animals were generally kept out of the living quarters. The roofs of the shed-type structures were made of bundled arrow weed laid on top of anything flat like pieces of tin, boards, or smaller willow logs.

Generally there were no rooms or inner partition walls as such. Partitions, if needed, were blankets or cloth hanging in place. The exterior walls were constructed of small willow or arrow weed shafts tied or nailed horizontally to the willow poles, over which a mud plaster made from clay dug from deposits in the river would be spread. This made for a fairly comfortable home which was quickly warmed in winter and only slightly cooler than outside air under the scorching summer sun. On those summer nights when the temperature might reach 100 degrees F. at midnight, the family would be found sleeping outdoors.

Sleeping outdoors, even if cooler, could be uncomfortable. Mosquitoes were thick on summer nights. The standard remedy was to burn pots of horse manure nearby, and while the smoke would burn ones eyes it also kept the mosquitoes at bay.

All cooking was done by wood fire using various types of wood. The best fires were made from hard mesquite wood which had been dried for a short period, and from a tree called "ironwood" which was found in the washes of the mesa west of the river. Its wood was so hard that an ax or hatchet would hardly nick a living tree. It was only after the tree had died and the wood was dry that it could be pulled over and dragged whole back to the house.

Cooking was usually done over an open fire with a piece of metal serving as a level cooking surface. The favorite bread for each meal was the tortilla, taken from their Mexican neighbors, made from a flour recipe mixed with lard and water, then hand shaped into small round doughballs. After a short "sit" time, the doughball was hand patted and pulled into a disc shape which could be anywhere between 8 and 12 inches in diameter and one-eighth of an inch thick, depending on attitude of the cook of the day.

The preferred cooking surface for the tortilla was a single shiny metal disc which had been discarded by a farmer off the farm implement used to break up the soil after plowing. The disc was of tempered steel, always shiny, and easy to clean. But the favorite of favorites was the bread called in Quechan, *muth-ku-thup'*, which was like a large 18-inch biscuit, only better, which was cooked by putting the specially-made dough into the hot earth underneath a fire, covering it with a layer of damp green leaves then with a layer of hot coals. It was so tasty to the boy that he later took it as his Indian name: Muth-ku-thup'.

There were two main methods of transportation for most Indian people. They could walk to wherever they were going, or use a horse. Most families had a team of horses which were used to plow small patches of land for a garden, and to pull a multi-use wooden wagon. It was not unusual to see a line of Indian wagons, each filled with adults and children on their way to Yuma on Saturday mornings. They would unhitch their horses on the eastern side of the river, then walk to Main Street for social visits with their Cocopah relatives who had also come to town from their own reservation some 20 miles south of Yuma.

Most of the younger unmarried men would prefer to walk to town dressed in their recently washed black or blue denim trousers and a white shirt which had been boiled and bleached. They almost never wore a shirt to town unless it was just freshly ironed.

Many of the Indian women would be driven to the Southern Pacific Railroad depot in Yuma. The transcontinental railroad had become a reality in 1870 and when Yuma became a tourist stopover point, the Indian women had begun a custom of meeting each train with their wares of distinctive black and red-colored Quechan pottery, beadwork of belts and necklaces made by the women, and miniature bows and arrows made by the men.

On their way home after a successful sales day, the wagons would stop at the Fort Yuma Grocery Store where Cy worked, for refreshment and a snack. (The grocery store was owned by a Mr. E. F. Sanguinetti of Yuma, who had hired Cy as a butcher, and another Quechan person to handle the gas, kerosene and oil business.)

The favorite snack of most of the Quechans seemed to be a thick slice of beef "baloney" and a small box of Sunshine crackers, topped off with a bottle of Nehi brand strawberry soda. Those Quechan who did not talk English would order the soda by just saying "Red." When they merely said "red" in any store in town, they would be handed a bottle of good ol' strawberry soda.

So, in the early 1930s, life was not too bad for the Quechan. It was not an easy life, but there seemed to be no depression here. There was no need for huge incomes, and yet they were not poor. What you could not buy, one simply did without. There were no utility bills or income taxes to pay, and one lived in one's own house on one's own land. Life was uncomplicated, but things in Washington, D.C. were happening and this would soon affect their uncomplicated lifestyle.

CHAPTER 9

SHARING THE WEALTH

The Quechan had never considered themselves as being poor. But the effect of the long national economic depression was spreading throughout the country. And politicians would fix it, they said. After the election of Franklin D. Roosevelt in 1932, federal officials soon began telling the Indians that they were poor. Until this time, they had not realized it. It is necessary to say that most of the approximately 1,000 people living on the Quechan reservation were still living as they had in the late 1800's, yet their main complaint was that the government was intruding in their tribal affairs. Much like today.

In the meantime, the family of Cy and Momma was much better off than most Indian and non-Indian families. From the sale of food, eggs and vegetables, she brought electricity to the house in the form of one single light bulb which hung from the ceiling. She bought a double socket so she could plug the brooder's heat bulb into one and still have the other for light. Then wonder of wonders, one day she no longer had to do the laundry by hand in a galvanized wash tub as she had for many years. She bought a Maytag electric washing machine, with a wringer yet. It was easy to use, but Allie would always get her arm caught in the wringer while feeding the laundry through it and would have to holler for help.

The children all had their own assigned chores around the house. The young boy's two main jobs were to fill the big tub with water and build a fire underneath it and bring it to a boil for the laundry. The other chore was to rake the front yard clean. The front yard had a hard dirt surface, so he would make a game of raking designs into the dirt in the manner seen in Japanese gardens. Most of the time he was free to roam the countryside with Jerry. He got into serious trouble once while playing with wooden matches.

He was striking matches on a small rock near the wheat field which his mother had planted, and now it was near time for harvesting. Somehow a spark landed in the nearest wheat plants and quicker than anything, a fire was burning in the wheat field. Momma came out of the house and screamed for help and began trying to beat the fire down with an old gunny (burlap) sack. Every car passing on the highway stopped and lent a hand and soon the fire was put out, but not before almost half of the field had burned. Needless to say, the boy had a sore behind for a few days. But his mother had always told him to be honest and "if you are wrong, take your punishment." This was a lesson that stayed with him throughout his lifetime.

Then later, Cy and Momma were able to buy a used Model T Ford automobile, which was probably more than five years old. There were no more than half a dozen families on the reservation able to afford a car, or even needed one. One had to use a crank handle to start it. Repairs and upkeep of the car was no problem. Anyone with a simple understanding of the simple ignition system or gas lines could make necessary repairs with nothing more than a pair of pliers and a piece of baling wire. A flat tire could be repaired on the spot with a rubber patch, a can of glue, and a tire pump. No big deal. Life was good. The only thing the boy wished for occasionally was when on trips into Yuma, which had paved streets and concrete sidewalks, was to have a pair of roller skates like the town kids had, or the Silver Streak bicycle which one boy was racing up and down Main Street. It was never to be.

But the most desirable thing that he wished for was a bright red metal wagon, which he just knew could be put to good use by hauling things around and bringing the groceries back from the store. He had even whispered his wish to Santa Claus when the family had gone into Yuma to see the huge Christmas tree set up on Main Street. More on this later, with perhaps a lesson: Be careful what you wish for.

CHAPTER 10

GOOD SAMARITAN OF THE DESERT.

The family home was located just off of the transcontinental highway number 80 which ran from Los Angeles to some far off point in the east, but who cared. The family was not going anywhere.

The steel bridge which now spanned the Colorado River, finally joining Arizona to California, had a large sign on its side which read "Ocean-To-Ocean Highway" followed by the word "YUMA," if one had any doubts about where they were.

Beginning about 1930 and continuing for several years, more and more highway travelers in all kinds of cars and beat up trucks crossed that bridge into California piled high with tables, chairs, beds, and household items, with Granny on top, looking exactly like the Clampett family in the Beverly Hillbillies. These people were refugees from the dust bowls of Oklahoma and Texas who were on their way to "the land of milk and honey" in California, as one man told them. A terrible drought in America's mid-West farmland region, coupled with the depression, had caused all these people to lose their farms, jobs, and businesses and now they had reached Quechan country.

They apparently didn't realize that they were already in California, so where was this promised land?

By the time they arrived at this California-Arizona border location on the Quechan reservation land, they first had to cross the hot desert areas of Texas, New Mexico, and Arizona. Their beat up cars and trucks, as well as their bodies, needed rest and repairs, and both children and adults were hot, tired, dirty and hungry.

One can only imagine the thoughts in their heads when they saw this little oasis which this Indian family had handy to them. There was a flat piece of land nearby with the inviting shade of a mesquite tree grove and a slowly flowing irrigation canal next to it where they could wash off the accumulated days or even weeks of grime from their bodies. Each day at least a half-dozen families would pull off the highway and ask Momma if they could camp there. Today, it is amazing that in those days even these poor tired people would first ask an Indian's permission to rest there. None of them were ever rude or discourteous to this Indian family.

Momma never refused free food and rest to any family. If they camped, she would provide them with a chicken, milk for the children, or a loaf of bread. She said, "The Okies are people just like us, only they don't have a home." She called them Okies, not as a pejorative, but she told the children that was where they were from, Oklahoma. The 1937 Hollywood movie, "Grapes of Wrath," depicted the Okie refugees exactly. One can wonder if any of the hundreds of families who stopped there and received her help, remembered what this "Good Samaritan of The Desert," this Indian woman, had done for them.

Remembered especially, is one family whose car needed extensive repairs so they stayed longer than most. They had a small girl possibly five years of age. Momma invited her to have dinner with the family several times. On her first visit, Momma served dinner to her first. She was really hungry. Allie asked her what she would like to drink, water or milk? She immediately answered "I'll have some White Horse." The adults broke out laughing because White Horse was the name of a Scotch whiskey. The children didn't know what they were laughing about. Momma then said that this is probably what her family called milk.

Another family named Johnson, stayed awhile so the father could work somewhere to earn some traveling money. They had two husky sons, the older, Junior, being about age six. He was the first to ever teach the boy something about cooking a meal. Using milk from the cow, a cup of flour, and little bit of lard he showed the boy how to make white gravy. That and a few tomatoes from the garden made a delicious lunch. Junior said that while his folks were away all day working in the fields, he had to cook for himself and his younger brother during the day. He told of the many places "back east" where he had been, with embellishments, for sure, but for the boy it was like reading a book about far away countries.

CHAPTER 11

A BOY AND HIS DOG

The Quechan reservation encompassed land on both sides of the river. The river banks and flood plains were covered with dense forests in which there was much for a young boy and his dog to explore. This was as new to them as the moon would be to astronauts decades later. Away from the river forests the land was covered with several kinds of brush which shared the space with groves of mesquite, salt cedar, and willow trees. Farther back yet was the rolling desert hills and rock formations, home of several kinds of cactus, poisonous sidewinder snakes, and many creatures of the night including scorpions, lizards, and birds of carrion.

On one day the boy and his dog would explore all that the river bank jungles held in secrecy; the next they would be testing their strength against the hot desert sands. One favorite desert spot was the nearby sand hills a few miles west of the river. These sand hills were Saharan in appearance and were later actually used as such in several major Hollywood movies: Beau Geste, Suez Canal, and others.

But the joy of these sand hills was in rolling down their sides then trying to climb back up, fighting the stream of sand which flowed down like water against the human effort to climb. It was such fun. On some Sundays, on father's day off, the family would spend a day in those sand hills. The shape of the hills were constantly changing because of the wind currents moving the sand from here to there. One day the boy's grandmother showed him one of the wonders of the sand hills. She searched the ridges for a time until she stopped and pointed out a flat-leafed plant which had about six broad leaves similar in shape to the water lily, yet living and growing here on a hot and dry pile of sand without water of any kind, seemingly.

The grandmother motioned for the boy to "just look at this wonderful thing." She gently began to move sand away from under the leaves and showed him a pale-colored single root, about the size and color of a parsnip, which she said could extend deep into the sand until it found water. If one would ever get lost, she said, this single root could provide both food and water for the traveler. An important lesson, if one would ever have the need.

Another favorite place was in the fast moving river water. The boy and his dog had learned to swim early on and the strong river currents held no fear for them. To be found in the fast currents were literally hundreds of fish swimming on the surface which made a sucking sound as they nibbled at the foam washed from plants along the river bank. The boy would swim into the school of fish and admire them while Jerry watched from the bank.

At other times, they would swim out to a sand island and look for deposits of slick black clay which lay in the river's bottom. The clay would be dug up in clumps, from which crude sculptures could be formed. A ball of clay was sometimes taken home for use by his aunt and grandmother. They used it for cleaning of their hair by rubbing it into the scalp, letting it dry, and then washing it clean with water.

The irrigation canal which ran past their home was another source of family fun. It was their own private swimming pool and was where the boy had learned to swim. Momma had tied a small rope around his waist, threw him in the water, and told him to "swim, swim." When the canal was only half full this added to the enjoyment because then there was enough water to swim and it was easier to hand dig into the slick black clay. With this clay, a slide could be made from the top edge of the canal and ending in the low water. Jerry, of course, joined in the fun and sometimes even the sow pig jumped in to enjoy the water and the mud.

The boy had learned how to make a slingshot from a forked mesquite branch and strips cut from an old rubber inner tube. On one day, he went "hunting" with Jerry through a mesquite grove when a gray dove flew out a tree ahead of him and wobbled along the ground like it had a broken wing. He aimed and hit the dove with a small pebble. The dove was dead, so he carried it back to a nest from where it had flown. In the nest he found several baby doves who were obviously waiting for their mother to return. Remorse struck him. He realized that the dove had pretended to have a broken wing in order to draw him away from the nest. He didn't know what to do with the baby doves, so he lay the dead mother dove back in the nest, but he swore then never to hunt a bird again. That vow is still intact. In fact, as an adult, he has never hunted a bird or an animal.

CHAPTER 12

FAMILY ENTERTAINMENT

Winter evenings in their home are still memorable to him. After a good supper, the boy would feed the leftovers to the sow and little pigs. His siblings had other chores to do before they could settle down to do school homework. Enough wood for the night would be brought in for the big black iron woodstove. The stove was used to cook all meals, boil water for dishwashing and baths, and it was their source of heat. On cold winter mornings the children would line up at the stove waiting for Momma to wash out their eyes with hot water because they would be stuck closed from the effects of an eye disease called "Pink Eye." They also lined up here to get their spoonful of castor oil, cod liver oil, or whatever Momma decided they needed. Family activity revolved around that stove. Water for washing of laundry was boiled in a large metal tub outdoors.

That woodstove attracted the boy, especially when water was put on to boil. There was a large kettle with a long spout on it in which water was heated. One evening when steam was coming out of that spout, the boy put his mouth over the spout to feel the steam and accidentally inhaled boiling water. It burned his vocal chords so that he could not talk for awhile and today he still cannot sing a full octave. Who knows, he might have been an opera star.

Prior to Momma bringing electricity to the house, light for supper and evening activities was provided by a coal oil lamp or two. It seemed to be all they needed. They had a Philco radio which operated off of a car battery. This was their entertainment center. They could listen to music and programs from radio stations KFI Los Angeles, KOA Denver, and even hear the Carter Family as they broadcast from far away Eagle Pass, Texas.

A nightly ritual was the short walk in the dark to the outhouse before bedtime. At one time they had gone separately to this outhouse until someone told Momma that they had seen a ghost out there. So from then on they walked in a tight bunch while someone held a kerosene lantern. After that no one actually saw the ghost, but they would scare each other by shouting, "There it is."

On top of Indian Hill, next to the Catholic Church, the federal Indian Health Service operated a small hospital and clinic for use by the Quechan. Although small, it was able to provide sufficient care for whatever accident or illness might occur. The boy had reason to use this twice. The first time was when he might have been four years of age. He had not started school yet.

On one summer night, the family listened to a news broadcast about a terrible war that was happening in two foreign countries. When the boy heard that people were being shot and were dying in the war, it created questions. He had never heard of "war" and he wondered why so many people were killing each other. The next morning, he was sitting on a wood fence near the house when Momma came out to hang laundry. He asked her about war, what was it and why were people being killed? From far away, it seemed, she answered him in some way but he could not remember what she said because everything seemed to go dark and the next time he awoke, he was in that hospital in a bed with crisp sheets. People were standing around the bed. He saw Momma, and there was Cy.

His father leaned over and told him that he was very sick, but that if he would try and get well, he would buy him the red metal wagon he had wished for at Christmas. After that he couldn't wait to get out of the hospital and go home. It was a long time afterwards that he learned that he had been ill from meningitis and had nearly died.

When he finally went home and saw the red wagon waiting for him in the front yard, he was so happy. It had side stakes on it and was fire engine red. Wagons like this and bicycles and other toys which children in town took for granted had always been unaffordable for Cy, but he had promised him the wagon if he would get well, and now he had kept his promise. The boy loved his father but could never bring himself to actually tell him so while he lived. Only on the day of Cy's funeral was he able to say the words. But that was the Quechan way, there were no words for love, only in actions and attitude.

For many weeks afterwards, the siblings would take turns riding that wagon down the hill on the main highway. They had to get up early in the morning before highway traffic would begin. It was up early, pull the wagon to the highway and ride down the hill for as long as no cars or trucks would come. They had to use the highway because the wagon would not roll down any of the dirt hills near the house.

CHAPTER 13

WHAT HAPPENS WHEN YOU DIE?

One evening when he and Jerry came home from their day of exploration, his mother told him that the next day everyone would be going to the cremation grounds for the beginning of a ceremony. He was to learn that this was a traditional remembrance of those relatives who have died during the past year. This annual ceremony was called "*Karuk*" (Karrook) and it is said that this ceremony ends the period of mourning for the deceased.

When a person dies and is cremated, the relatives save some of the deceased's clothing which will be used later at the *Karuk* when it is put on a wooden image of the deceased. The life-sized image would in the old days be made of willow or cottonwood. The *Karuk* is held for four days and four nights and it begins during a certain phase of the moon so that a full moon would be shining during the final night when the images would be made to appear to be dancing with their relatives. Near the conclusion in early morning, the images are carried in a procession towards the east then to the south, where they are finally laid upon a pile of dry arrow weed and willow logs.

The cremation fire is then lit and the images are committed to the fire in their final tribute. Relatives then dance circling the fire, and put gifts of clothing or personal items into the flames which will be carried up in the smoke to the relative in the other world.

For the Quechan, Mojave, and Cocopah tribes, all neighbors on the river, the cremation is important to their beliefs. It is said that if a person's body is not cremated the spirit will wander around and talk to its relatives in dreams. Unique to the Quechan is the belief that after cremation the spirit does not go at once to the other place because it is "too young and inexperienced" to travel so it lingers four days near its former home. After that it can see its way and then goes to the home of the spirits.

There is a great difference in the cremation ceremony for a chief or leader of the tribe and for a common tribal member. The cremation ceremony for a tribal member can be done and over in as little as one day. For a chief, it can last four days with the singing of special songs and long speeches throughout the day and nights. Two exceptions to the rule for common tribal members have been documented. The first occurred in 1921. A young Quechan man had been killed by Germans during World War I. He had enlisted in the U.S. Army, and became the first American Indian to die in that war. Buried in France, his body was later exhumed and brought home in 1921 for cremation.

Every Quechan knew he was on his way home, so preparations were begun. For several weeks before he arrived, each Saturday and Sunday the people gathered and sang their songs for him. When his body arrived at the Southern Pacific depot in Yuma, it was met by a large crowd. For a full week before his cremation, there was continuous singing and dancing. Sometimes three or four singing groups were singing different songs at the same time. This was unusual. Mojave and Quechan bird songs were sung as were songs of the Sun, the Frog, and the Raven. Hand games and other games were played during the night.

The second cremation ceremony of note was that of another veteran of World War I who died in 1975. He had been a Musician First Class in the U.S. Navy. He was a part of the Quechan Indian Band which was known far and wide among the southwest Indian tribes. The Quechan Indian Band had performed throughout the nation in the late 1920's and early 1930's, once in a national tour and at two World Fairs. They were the most famous thing that the Quechan tribe had to offer at that time. Other tribes had their own brass bands and the Quechan would many times perform with them in state and local functions. This man had made many friends whereever he had gone.

He died in April of 1975 and his cremation was planned to take place at the Quechan reservation. The ceremonies, singing and dancing lasted for four days and four nights, and people, Indians and non-Indians, came from throughout the southwest to say good-bye to him. At funerals for band members, it had become customary that the Quechan Band play a concert each day in honor of the deceased, with an empty chair at his usual place in the band. The band also leads the procession on the final walk to the cremation pyre. All of the deceased's favorite marches, overtures, and hymns are played in a final tribute.

On the final night of this particular ceremony, there were three separate singing groups singing at the same time and there were many women dancers swaying in rhythm with the singers. The body lay on a hospital-type single bed with an American flag draped over it. In the final hours of the singing and dancing, just before daybreak, it was an eerie sight to see the draped flag moving in rhythm with the singers. It was apparently caused by the many singers and dancers moving together that made the flag move as it did, but again, maybe not. The deceased had been honored as a very important person and perhaps he had acknowledged the honor.

During funeral ceremonies, women of the tribe gather and cook for the participants and visitors, many of them staying there all day and night. At certain periods, friends and relatives of the deceased will circle the gathering, passing in front of the family members and shaking their hands in condolence and sharing a kind word with them. It is common for both men and women to approach the body and in loud cries tell of their friendship and respect for the deceased and to stand with the immediate family and join them in their crying and shedding of tears for their loss. It is also common for even those who are not a close relative of the deceased to express their sorrow for the family to stand with them and to cry with them.

When the head man decides it is time for the procession, there will be a last period of loud wailing and crying while the selected men prepare the body and personal belongings for the procession. The singers will lead the procession in a slow walk, singing all the while, and stopping about every fifty feet until reaching the pyre. The body is removed from the bed, or in the absence of a bed, a carrying blanket, and placed in the prepared place within the pyre. The pyre is made of dry willow logs surrounded by bundles of dry arrow weed. After one last good-bye and touching of the body, it is then covered over with more willow logs. After a final speech by the head man, a special person will apply a burning arrow weed torch to the pyre. The fire is so intense that it is usually burned down within thirty minutes. Within hours nothing will remain of the pyre site and the ground cover will show no sign of what happened here. If this person had been selected to be honored at the "release of the spirit" *Karuk* ceremony, one person will save a part of the clothing to be worn by the image.

After the cremation is over, mourners and singers fast for four days, eating little as possible with no salt or grease. The name of the dead person is not spoken until it is spoken at the *Karuk* ceremony.

CHAPTER 14

BOYS WILL BE BOYS

At ceremonies of this kind as well as occasionally scheduled social dance gatherings, there would be several wood fires which would burn all night, for light as well as for heat, and it would be the duty of the young boys to make sure that wood was placed on the fires to keep them burning continually. It is curious that in the 1930's, in between their fire maintenance duties, the boys played games in the dark and one of those games most popular at the time was that of "cowboys and Indians," with most boys preferring to play the part of their favorite white movie hero such as Tom Mix, Ken Maynard, Bob Steele, and other well known cowboy "good guys."

As mentioned before, the area was popular with Hollywood movie-makers. Before Jerry had joined the family, they had somewhere acquired a Dachshund dog. The children's momma told them it was a "weenie dog" and it went everywhere with them. One day there was a movie company filming a horse chase scene just below the Methodist Mission church not far from the family home. The young boy went to watch. In the scene, cowboy good-guy Tom Mix was riding his horse fast down a dirt trail chasing a bad-guy. When the cowboy and his horse ran past a point near the boy and his dog, the dog lunged at the horse and was kicked in the head by the horse's hoof. The dog died immediately and the boy ran home with the dog in his arms and told Momma that he didn't want to see any more movies being made.

A few years later he changed his mind when the Beau Geste crew came and brought a herd of camels with them which they corralled near the family home. The boy was paid ten cents each day for carrying water to the camels. He had, of course, never seen an animal like the camel and he was awestruck. By this time in his life, at eight years of age, he was an altar boy at the St. Thomas Catholic Church and when the full movie cast arrived and began filming at the sand hills, on Sunday's he and two other altar boys went with Father Felix to their sand hills camp to say mass for the film crew and then to have lunch with them. Gary Cooper was one of the stars whom he got to meet, but he was most impressed by the beautiful lunch which was prepared for them. He had never seen such a pretty table with so much good food piled high on it. He looked forward to Sunday's until the film crew left town.

CHAPTER 15

SCHOOL DAZE

Many things happened during this period of growing up in the 1930's. When he was five, his mother had taken him into the town of Yuma and registered him in the first grade of the public school. He was the only Indian boy in this school, but he had little problem in adjusting to the new experience. On his first day, at his first morning recess period, a girl by the name of Muriel Buckalew came to him and said she would show him around the school, how to use the drinking fountain, where the bathrooms were and tell him what the different bells meant. Even to this day it amazes him to remember this act of kindness on the part of a six-year-old "white girl."

But he learned quickly, as he did throughout his life, and was soon reading so well that on the way home from school he would stop at the City Library and pick up a book for home reading. His favorites were the Wizard of Oz series, Bomba the Jungle Boy series, and best of all the Tarzan of the Jungle books. He read so well that in class, his teacher said he could not really read, that he had merely memorized what his mother had read to him. She sent a note home to Momma asking her not to read to him anymore. Everyone at home got a good laugh out of this. In fact, he found it fun to confound carnival barkers when they came to town twice a year.

At least one barker on the carnival midway would entertain the crowd by having some small boy try to repeat after him when he made up sentences using long and unfamiliar (to most of the crowd) words. Once when the barker asked for some "little boy" to come help him, the boy jumped at the chance and stood there while the barker asked him to "repeat after me." The barker could say nothing that he couldn't repeat exactly and the crowd would roar. After doing this several times the novelty wore off because it was so easy.

One day when he had walked home from school in a hot, burning sun, he was surprised to see that his father was already home and waiting for him. He explained that Jerry, his red mutt dog, was dead and that he had either been poisoned or had been bitten by a rattlesnake. The boy said nothing, holding his tears until he could be alone. But he knew that he and Jerry had roamed the jungles and the desert and had never been threatened by any kind of snake. He was convinced that someone had poisoned Jerry, "probably some Mexican or white man" that didn't like Jerry, he thought. But he promised Jerry's spirit that he would never forget him, and he has not. Jerry lives on in memory.

CHAPTER 16

THE FAMILY BREAKUP

Not long after Jerry died, he began to notice that on some days Momma was not home when he got there. Sometime in the late afternoon, his father would drive in and help Momma into the house where she would begin making supper. This happened more and more and one time she was gone for a week. Yet no one told him what was happening.

A few months later, the children were told that Momma was sick and the family would move to a more comfortable house located at the rear of the Fort Yuma Tourist Court (the precursor of modern motels). It was a better house with separate bedrooms for boys and girls and most important, a large separate bedroom for Cy and Momma. Still the boy didn't realize how sick Momma was.

One night he woke up startled to hear his mother screaming in pain and his father trying to soothe her with comforting words. He lay there frightened. At first this happened occasionally and then more frequently until it was a daily event. Cy's sister and her husband said they could hear her screams from their house nearby. In those days the most effective pain killer used was morphine, but the body would develop a tolerance for it thereby decreasing its effectiveness. At a certain point, Momma had to endure the excruciating pain.

One day his father told him and his younger sisters that Momma had cancer and that they had tried to treat her at different hospitals, including the now well-known Loma Linda Cancer Center near Los Angeles. But the treatments were not working and that Momma now wanted to go home to Isleta, New Mexico to die there. There came the day when Cy fixed a bed in the back seat of the family car. Early the next morning, before the younger children woke, Cy carried Momma out and placed her on the back seat bed, and with older sister Allie with him, he began the long drive to Isleta, where after a blessing by a Pueblo holy man she died and was buried in the Isleta cemetery. Her legacy to her five children was a determination to succeed by working hard and to have confidence in themselves. An important chapter in the boy's life had ended. This event had an effect on Allie and she went on to become a Registered Nurse and spent her lifetime taking care of sick and suffering Indian people. Sadly, she died of cancer herself in 1987.

Jerry was gone and now Momma was gone, and what the boy didn't know was that the family would soon be broken up. The sweet life as a boy had ended. He would soon have to be a man.

CHAPTER 17

LIFE WITHOUT MOMMA

His father was a broken man after Momma died. He might have blamed himself for her death, because Momma had once asked him to get another car, one that she didn't have to crank to start it running. Those early cars had a tendency to "kick" the crank backwards if there was too much compression and too little spark for ignition. One day it did kick back and hit Momma in the groin area. She later said this is what caused her illness. Perhaps, but it is possible that Cy blamed himself and in any case, he told the children that he was going to another town to get a better job. Much later, as an adult, the boy could understand why his father had not been able to cope with Momma's death. He would leave them all in the care of his sister and her husband.

Their aunt and uncle had four children of their own, but in Indian society it is usual for grandparents or other relatives to take care of children left alone. They were told it would not be for long.

Older brother Al was now about 14 and assumed responsibility for the others. For the younger boy, this opened up new experiences. He was now in the fifth grade in the Yuma public school. The local BIA agency had been paying tuition for some Quechan children to attend public school in Yuma where the educational system was much better than at the Fort Yuma Indian School. For some unexplained reason, now the BIA would no longer pay for that public school education. (BIA payments were in lieu of tax payments to the city)

Uncle had a good education and had even gone to Carlisle College in Pennsylvania. He obviously knew the value of an education and he knew the Agency Superintendent. He arranged for Al, and sisters Allie, Lily and Marie, to attend a Catholic school, St. Catherine's, near Santa Fe, New Mexico. The young boy would stay with his aunt and uncle and attend the Fort Yuma Indian School for now.

In September, 1938, he was registered at the Fort Yuma Indian School where the level of education was very low and he was placed in the seventh grade. For instance, arithmetic was at about the third grade level of that in public school. Half of the school day, for seventh and eighth grade boys, was spent in learning carpentry and farming. He tried carpentry and hated it after he had almost cut off a finger on the band saw, so he turned to the farming project where he was taught how to raise vegetables and to market them by carrying baskets of them from house to house selling them cheaply to white housewives. He liked the work because it was outdoors and he had already learned some gardening from his mother.

For two years he tolerated the Fort Yuma Indian School. His uncle had told him that after he finished the eighth grade, he would probably go to a boarding school in Riverside, California. All of uncles three sons had gone to school there and had been taught a skilled trade. In the meantime, he was enjoying his new, and temporary, freedom at this school. But he hated the daily music class taught by Mrs. Carson. She had a shrill singing voice and when she tried to get the 25 Indian students to join in, it was comical. The students could hardly keep from laughing out loud when Mrs. Carson stoutly banged on her piano while trying to get them to sing with her in a rendition of the Scottish song, "My heart's in the highlands, my heart is not here, etc." Everyone, including Mrs. Carson, must have been relieved when this half-hour was over.

The boys real love was for music, marching band music, the kind that had made the Quechan Indian Band famous. He had grown up with this. As mentioned before, most of these Quechan bandsmen had been the band aboard the Navy's U.S.S. California. He could remember when he was very small, getting on a bus with his father and 35 other men to travel to another town for a parade or a concert performance. On summer Saturday nights, the band would give concerts on

Indian Hill for the entire community. The rich from Yuma would drive over to hear them, and from the other side of the Hill the Indians would arrive in their wooden wagons or by walking. It was something enjoyed by people of all races, rich or poor.

The boy had gotten his start when he was about five. At one of the weekly band practices held at the Methodist Church, his father had given him an alto horn and sat him down among the men. He told him to "play." This was his first time to hold a brass instrument, so he watched what the men were doing and imitated them. He took the alto horn home and within a few weeks he was able to sustain real notes.

The Quechan Band was known for its distinctive uniforms: bell-bottomed dark blue Navy trousers altered to put a bright gold stripe down the sides, and which had silver concho's or silver dollars sewn onto the stripe. There was a red-trimmed short panel in front and back at the waist to remind one of the time when panels like that had been the only item of clothing worn by Quechan men a hundred years earlier. Their shirt was one of bright red cotton with beaded arm bands which had many colorful ribbons hanging from the bands. The uniform was completed with a fine headdress which each bandsmen made themselves. The feathers were genuine eagle feathers. They were indeed a beautiful group.

The City of Yuma was proud of the Quechan Band, even though they were Californians. In fact, for many years the band was known as the Yuma Indian Band. In those days, borders didn't matter as much as they do today. On special holidays like Armistice Day, November 11, the parade in Yuma would begin with a distinguished looking man in a World War I officers uniform leading the way. Main Street would be so crowded with people that it seemed everyone for miles around and from even Mexico had come to see the famous Yuma Armistice Day Parade. The local High School Band and others from surrounding communities would do their bit, but the main attraction, as every Quechan knew for a fact, was the Yuma Indian Band.

Main Street began to the west near the banks of the Colorado River. This was the formation area for the Quechan group, which would include a float from the Methodist Indian Mission, a small group of Indians and Anglo's representing the Catholic Church, Indian women in their finest beaded and be-ribboned silk or satin long dresses, and the band.

Listeners nearby the official reviewing stand would suddenly hear the loud combined musical sounds of the Quechan Band's sousaphones, tubas, baritones, and trombones as they boomed out the first notes of a parade favorite, "Them Basses." They could be heard before they were even seen, and everyone knew, "here comes the Yuma Indian Band." They were on parade, and the Quechan were proud. Unfortunately, few pictures of the band exist today because as was the Quechan custom, personal items of the deceased were placed on funeral pyres to take with them to the "other place."

On these special occasions the band might number as many as 50, with Quechans who worked in other cities coming home to participate. It was a special sight to see the first row of musicians coming down the street with feathers and ribbons flying. The first row was made up of five trombones, one of whom was the boy's father. They would be followed by as many as ten rows of Quechan bandsmen. The Band stayed intact until about 1970, when deaths and old age began to thin their ranks.

Before entering the fourth grade his father gave him a trumpet and said that when school started in Yuma, he could join the school band class. This is where he learned the ABC's of music. He was small in stature and his arms were a little short to always hold the trumpet upright and level, so Miss Haugen, the music teacher, was always tapping his fingers with her baton, reminding him to "hold it up, hold it up."

There was no band music class at the Fort Yuma Indian School, so when he attended school there, his only practice was when he would take the horn to a lonely spot on Saturday and Sunday afternoons and play to his hearts content. He would even compose marches in his mind which he would play loud and long.

In September of 1940, his uncle registered him for school at Sherman Institute, which was a boarding school for Indians in Riverside, California. By this time, older brother Al had graduated from High School, transferred to Sherman Institute, and was attending the Riverside Junior College. His sisters were still going to school in New Mexico. He had not seen them for three years and would not see them for several more. It would be more than six years before he would return to his homeland.

Today Sherman Institute is now called Sherman Indian High School and is purely academic in curriculum. Prior to about 1950, the school was used as a vocational boarding school where Indians from throughout the western states could learn a useful trade and a basic education. There was a policy, though, that students from or near an urban area received a standard state high school education, while others from rural areas would receive only the basics of math and English while spending half of their school hours in learning a trade. They could change trades every semester if they chose, so it was possible that by graduation time, one could be fairly knowledgeable of several trades.

World War II began in December of 1941, and the Indian boys at Sherman wanted to go right away to join the military. Those over 17 years of age went immediately, mostly into the Marine Corps. The boy had to wait until 1943 when he turned 17 in March. By this time his father had settled down in Parker, Arizona. He asked for permission to join the Navy, his father agreed, so he signed up with a reporting date in May. Two days after his high school graduation ceremonies he was sworn in as a Navy recruit.

He had requested to serve as a musician or as a tailgunner on a torpedo plane, but instead he was put into training as a radioman. For the next three years, he found that his boyhood experiences had prepared him for this time. He served as a Radioman, then finally in 1945 he got his first wish when he was allowed to join the Treasure Island Navy Band in San Francisco. But even then he had to work for that by first volunteering to play Taps at the dozens of military funerals which took place every day at cemeteries throughout San Francisco and Oakland. The war's dead were returning in large numbers.

When he played in the Treasure Island Navy Band in his first full-dress review parade, he thanked his father and mother for all they had given him. It was a splendid parade, with flags flying briskly in the ocean breeze. He was sure all of his relatives were proud of him on this beautiful day. It was a great day for "One Little Indian."

END OF AN ERA

The boy, who was now a man, returned to Fort Yuma in 1946. He was shocked and saddened to see what the federal government had done to his homeland. He had sailed the Pacific, the South Pacific, the Indian and the Atlantic oceans, participating in two island invasions for his country, and this was his reward? The once thick and beautiful jungle of trees where he and Jerry had roamed was no longer in existence. The many groves of mesquite and the fields of green arrow weed had disappeared. The U.S. Army Corps of Engineers had decided that the trees used up too much water and had to be cut down so that there would be water for the huge orange groves in Arizona. The Colorado River, once mighty and majestic, was now only a trickle of its former self. Upstream dams built to produce power and divert irrigation water had reduced the river to only inches deep and barely 50 feet wide. It was almost too much to bear.

He wept as he looked down from Indian Hill to what had once been his. Now only barren land was there. This was the end of an era, he thought. The beginning of the end for a generation of

Quechans who would be the last to remember what it was like in "the old days." It was a time for great sadness. In-ti-yah wept for her people, but She whispered to him, "Be patient and work hard."

He thought about all the hard work it would take to rebuild the reservation as he had known it. He had heard of a new law called The G. I. Bill which would help veterans to get loans for new homes and new businesses. It could be done, he told himself. Hadn't most of the Quechan young men volunteered to fight for the country? Almost a third of them had died for the country. Surely, with government help it could be done. When he was discharged from the Navy in a few weeks, he would get things started.

But he hadn't known of how politics and federal agencies worked. He hadn't known that while the Quechan men were away helping to fight a war, politicians in Washington, D.C. had tried to terminate the existence of Indian tribes. He and other veterans who sought G. I. Bill loans for tractors and other equipment, home and economic development loans, soon found that veterans who lived on Indian reservations were not eligible for such helpful loans. It was almost forty years later that the G. I. Bill was made to apply to Indian veterans living on reservations.

In fact, now that the Quechan had visions and plans of their own for development projects on the reservation, non-Indian farmers and other town folks who had formerly tolerated the Quechan became afraid of the possibility of new competition and they lobbied their politicians to stop any spending of federal money for the Quechan, saying publicly that any Quechan business was sure to fail and would be a waste of money. Discrimination had come to the southwest in a big way.

A few years earlier, the young boy had faced a critical turning point in his life, and in 1946 the Quechan people as a whole, were about to face a similar turning point. Their reputation as fighters was borne out as they turned to the battle at hand using the new weapons of education and the legal process. As this story is written in 1996 the Quechan have survived by not winning major victories, but by a slower process of winning the smaller battles, one at a time, just as In-ti-yah had originally taught them to do.

The young boy of this story went on to become a leader of the Quechan people, helping to win back thousands of acres of land that were illegally taken from them, winning the legal rights to thousands of acre-feet of Colorado River water for their own use, and bringing new economic development projects to the reservation. In doing so, he necessarily became involved in the national political process and was instrumental in the development of helpful legislation for Native Americans in the 1970's and 1980's.

 94

Once, in 1983, at a time when he was the leader of a powerful national Indian organization in Washington, D.C., when interviewed by the New York Times and asked why it was that Native American reservations were not getting rich, he said "We Indians are not about getting rich, we want to first create jobs with wages for the people. Profit, if any is to be, will come as a result of the creation of those jobs." This was in keeping with what he had been taught, that the welfare of one's people is more important than any wealth.

For a majority of Indian tribes, including the Quechan, sustainable economic growth has not yet arrived. This is a challenge for the new generation, those who do not remember "how things used to be." For them the future has not yet arrived. For those who remember, they counsel that the past must not be forgotten.

A view of the Quechan reservation from on top of Indian Hill. Picacho Peak can be seen in the background.

The Methodist Indian Mission as seen from the family home.

A view of the Quechan reservation from Indian Hill.